Map of the realm (runic inscription at top, untranslated)

Worlds End

The Raging Sea

C'Myxx

Neozord Mountains
Gwaldar's Shack
Roane
Castle Phereaux
Xellos

The Isle of Quaint Monsters

Vale of Desolation

L'Azaki
K'rby

M'Scaat

Niall's House
Mountains of Mystic Mists

Weirdling Woods

Isle of Strange Enchantments
Tothe
Pol Rhyts
P'Cry Rssyll

Brry K'tsyn

Worlds End

The Swirling Sea

The Sea of Storms

Floating Statues

Su'Mktygge

L'Galle

B'Ng

Isle of The Dark Ones
Mongroth

The Raging Mountains

A'Gyuss

Worlds' End

Volume 1 ~ The Riders on the Storm

STORY & ART
TIM PERKINS

Wizards Keep
PUBLISHING

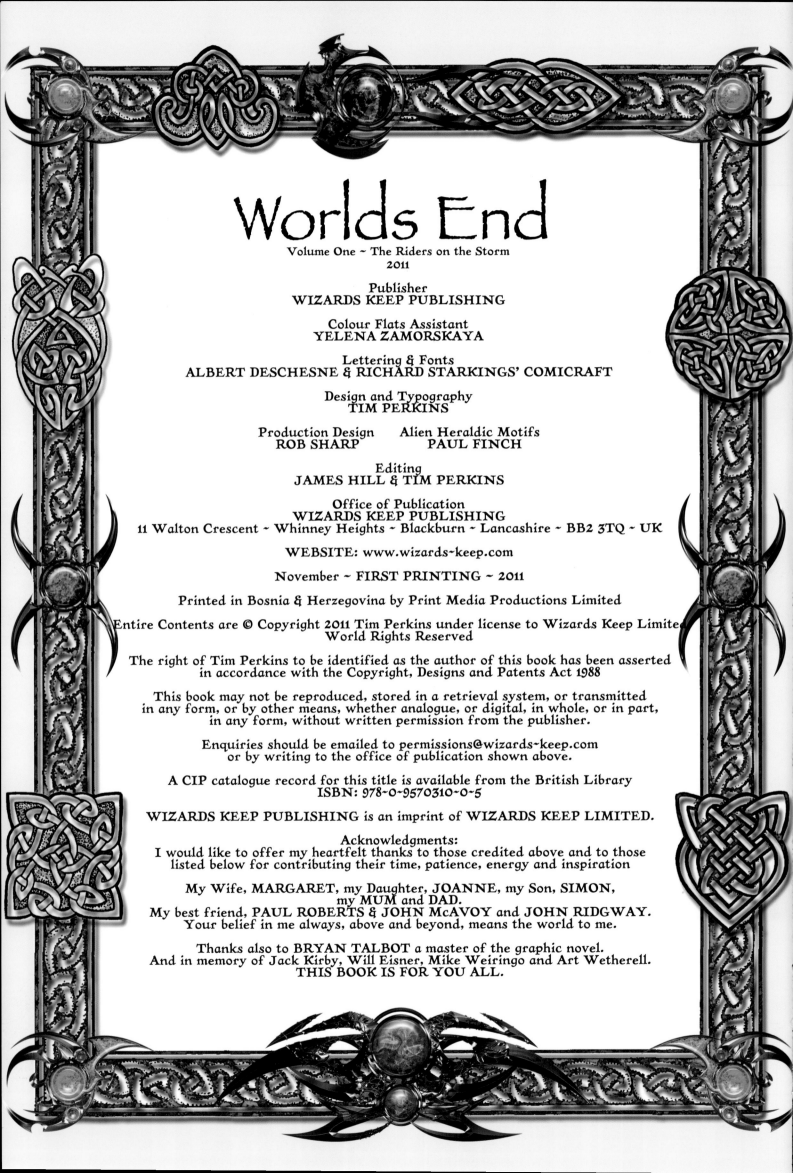

Worlds End

Volume One ~ The Riders on the Storm
2011

Publisher
WIZARDS KEEP PUBLISHING

Colour Flats Assistant
YELENA ZAMORSKAYA

Lettering & Fonts
ALBERT DESCHESNE & RICHARD STARKINGS' COMICRAFT

Design and Typography
TIM PERKINS

Production Design   Alien Heraldic Motifs
ROB SHARP   PAUL FINCH

Editing
JAMES HILL & TIM PERKINS

Office of Publication
WIZARDS KEEP PUBLISHING
11 Walton Crescent ~ Whinney Heights ~ Blackburn ~ Lancashire ~ BB2 3TQ ~ UK

WEBSITE: www.wizards~keep.com

November ~ FIRST PRINTING ~ 2011

Printed in Bosnia & Herzegovina by Print Media Productions Limited

A CIP catalogue record for this title is available from the British Library
ISBN: 978~0~9570310~0~5

WIZARDS KEEP PUBLISHING is an imprint of WIZARDS KEEP LIMITED.

Acknowledgments:
I would like to offer my heartfelt thanks to those credited above and to those
listed below for contributing their time, patience, energy and inspiration

My Wife, MARGARET, my Daughter, JOANNE, my Son, SIMON,
my MUM and DAD.
My best friend, PAUL ROBERTS & JOHN McAVOY and JOHN RIDGWAY.
Your belief in me always, above and beyond, means the world to me.

Thanks also to BRYAN TALBOT a master of the graphic novel.
And in memory of Jack Kirby, Will Eisner, Mike Weiringo and Art Wetherell.
THIS BOOK IS FOR YOU ALL.

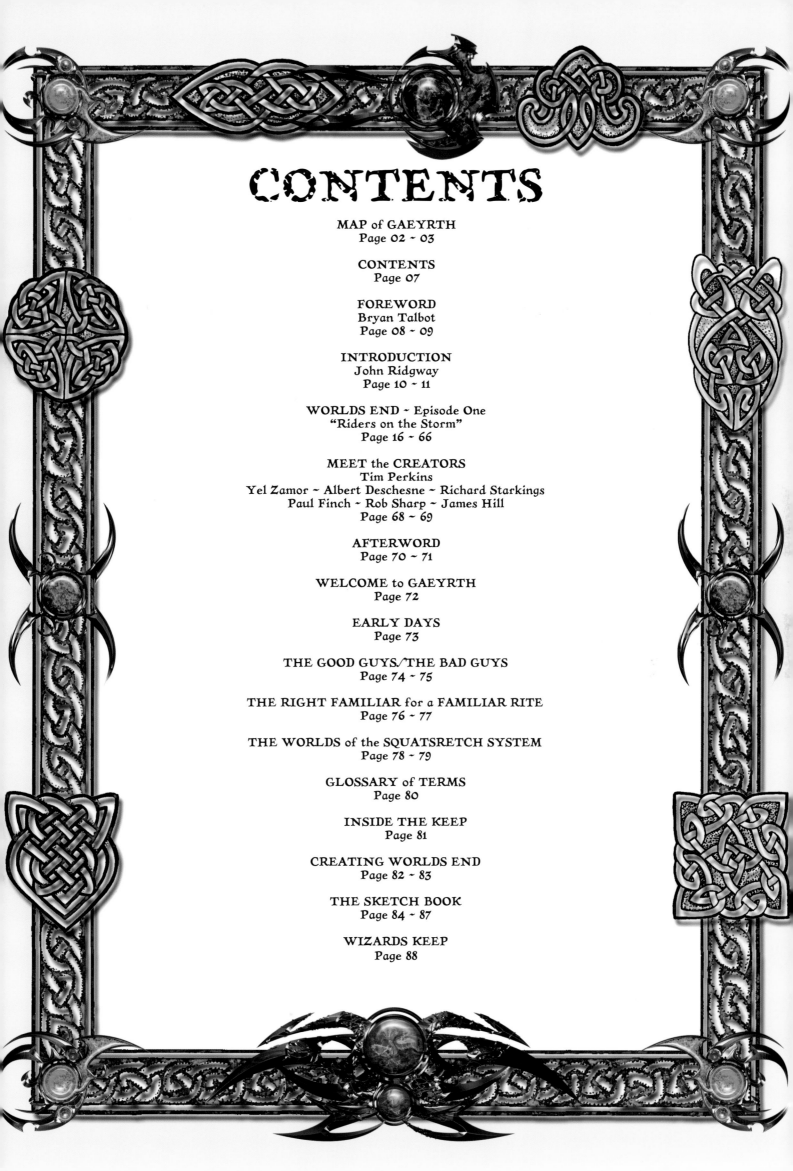

CONTENTS

Foreword
By Bryan Talbot

The vast majority of English language comics churned out by the large publishing conglomerates are the products of a production line. The scripts are provided by freelance writers, usually to a style dictated by the company's house style and the whims of an editor, the pencils drawn by one artist, inked by a second, lettered by a third and coloured by one or two others. The publishers have it printed and distributed and the profits go to their shareholders. It's a pretty soulless procedure, only redeemed by the creativity and skill of the contributors. The best comics produced by these companies are good despite, not because of, this process. Everything depends upon the quality of the writers and artists.

Tim Perkins has been a quality artist in the comic industry for over a thirty-year period and I think that I've known him almost as long. He's worked on a wide range of titles from Doctor Who, Transformers and 2000AD to The Beano and I once had the pleasure of him inking a miniseries I wrote for Teknocomics.

With Worlds End, he's done something different from the soulless norm I described above. Becoming a true comics creator, he's crafted something purely his own, a science fantasy adventure with heroism and comedy, evil and hope and, more than that, bar the lettering, it's entirely a product of Tim's own talent and craft. And, following in the footsteps of other writer-artists of successful fantasy comics, such as Jeff (Bone) Smith, Dave (Cerebus) Sim and Richard and Wendy (Elfquest) Pini, he's taken the bold step of publishing the book himself.

This is no mass-produced piece of big business commercialism but a genuine labour of love.

Bryan Talbot
Author of the Grandville
graphic novels

Introduction

By John Ridgway

As an artist I know that, in comics, sometimes a dream job comes along ~ a job that sparks your imagination, something to get your teeth into, a true pleasure to work on. But those occasions are rare, all too often marred by story~telling constraints. Stories for a magazine, for instance, may have to be fitted into 6~page chunks, often calling for the story to be stretched or compressed for each episode. An artist is lucky if he has an agreement with a writer or editor that he can split or combine pictures or move them to the next or previous page to allow a picture to be emphasised. All too often caption boxes get in the way or dialogue balloons interfere with, or dictate, the position of characters in a picture. If you work on a series created by another, you are constrained by the earlier artist's vision.

There is only one way to ensure that the perfect job can come about: create it yourself. Not only that: produce it as a graphic novel or graphic album. That way the only constraints on the number of pages and the pacing is up to you ~ no need to pad it out, no shoehorning it into a given space, just let it run free, its length determined only by the story itself and the page layouts you want to encompass. And yet, this is the simple part. Take a look at the credits on any comic from the American

big two publishers. There will almost always be a writer, a penciller, an inker, and a colourist. Each one of these 'chores' is a discipline in itself ~ each one capable of wrecking a comic if that person does not know their job.

For Worlds End, Tim has had to master all those disciplines ~ not only the obvious ones for an artist, but the very different discipline of writing; for it is one thing to give characters suitable expressions and stances, it is a vastly different thing to give them suitable dialogue, in character, not too long, clear and concise.

There is a further complication added to all this ~ the lack of a deadline (other than that imposed by Tim upon himself). There are two sides to a deadline. The obvious one is the time constraint (Am I going to finish the job in time?). The other side is more subtle.

Most artists worth their salt are never satisfied with what they do. I, for one, can only look at my work and see the faults. Without a deadline, the artist will go back to the work time and time again to make minute alterations ~ a never ending, pointless process, because nothing is ever perfect. A deadline prevents that. It makes you call time. When the only deadline is that imposed by oneself it takes an enormous discipline to say, "That's it ~ if I don't stop now, no~one is ever going to see this."

To me, the impact of a page is all~important ~ the 'Wow!' factor, the thing that stops you in your tracks when you first turn to a page. If you are thumbing through a graphic album in a shop and a page suddenly makes you stop and grabs your attention, you are far more likely to buy that

book. It is the thing that makes you come back to a page again and again. The 'Wow!' factor doesn't have to be a fight scene or an explosion. It can be something quiet and gentle ~ a beauty that takes your breath away. Tim's story has all the fight scenes and explosions you could want, but, importantly, it has the gentleness of human warmth and care to remind us of what the central characters are fighting for.

Many comics created today are filled with bitter characters, full of angst, railing against the darkness of the world they live in. Worlds End is not like that. Yes, it features a world in terrible danger and facing disaster, but through it all Tim's heroes still retain their humanity.

I've known Tim and Tim's work for a long time. I love the colours he uses: sometimes bright and cheerful, other~times soft pastille shades. The characters in his paintings are warm and alive, quaint and filled with the humour that fills Tim himself. He loves nature and he loves fantasy. The scenes on his Wizards Keep website often reflect that ~ woodlands and forests filled with gnarly trees that have cheerful faces smiling out at you, cottages without a single straight line, giant red mushrooms (or toadstools ~ I can never tell which is which), and cascading waterfalls.

Worlds End contains no smiling trees (at least none yet ~ so far as I'm aware) but it is a beautiful, cheerful world. This, however, is only the starting point, for this is a world at risk.

This is a story for kids ~ and I'm a kid at heart. Not just for kids of my age, but for my kids and their kids. I've watched this story develop. There is an immense amount of work in here, an incredible amount of detail to linger over as we,

the readers, travel with Gweldar, the ingenious inventor, Geek (a furry something), Ralf (definitely a young hero in the making) and Zephol (ready to set Ralf right if he puts a foot wrong), from what is friendly and familiar to places that are harsh and cruel. And yet, it is a simple story. The good guys are good, but they are in a minority and have to dig deep to find the bravery they never needed before ~ and, probably, never realized they had. I don't think there's a nasty bone in their bodies. They have the courage to face adversity that we hope we could find in ourselves, should the need arise ~ heaven forbid. The bad guys are bad ~ thoroughly bad ~ and there are a lot of them in all shapes and sizes, and they need to be sorted out.

This is a story about those who love life and nature against those who would twist a world to their own ends without a care for those who suffer ~ the individual (and friends) against the might of the faceless, soulless corporation.

Knowing Tim, I'm fairly confident that the good guys will win out in the end ~ and it will be a fun ride along the way.

John Ridgway
Artist: Age of Heroes

"This is for everyone
who has ever looked at the stars
or gazed from atop of a hill
or across the sea
and wondered..."

DO NOT READ THIS BOOK!

Once you start down this tortuous path there will be no turning back. The path is an adventurous one – and one from which you may not be able to return. For the distance between here and there will be both long and arduous.

If you choose to ignore this dire warning then, like the heroes you will find within, you will have to pit your wits against the most terrible of enemies... The Aoevill.

The choice is now yours; I hope you make the right one and an enjoyable one.

Please forgive me if the book you now hold in your hands is too exciting.

Your scribe,
Signature here .... Tim Perkins
Tim Perkins

Once upon a time...

On the third planet from the outer rim of the Squatsretch system lies a world untainted by evil. Its myriad inhabitants going about their daily lives without worry or fear...

...that is, until today...

16

OHMYGOODNESS! I HOPE TH'LAD IS OKAY... IF I STOP I'LL NOT BE ABLE TO WARN ANYONE ABOUT THESE CREEPS!

COME ON, GEEK ≥PUFF≤ TRY AN' KEEP UP!

THEY ARE ALMOSsST IN OUR GRASsSP!

I'M RUNNING ≥PUFF≤ OUT OF ≥PANT≤ STEAM. THIS CALLS ≥PUFF≤ FOR A CONTINGENCY PLAN.

YEEP... YEEEEPP!

TIME FOR DRASTIC MEASURES! TASTE SOME ELDRITCH MAGIK, MY FRIENDS! GET THEE HENCE, FOUL DOGS...

STAND THEE DOWN, FOUL BLIGHT!

YEEEEPEEEE!

MAGIC TRICKSsss! WATCH OUT!

DEFEAT THE OLD ONE, WE MUSsST! AFTER HE ISsss TAKEN, HISsss FAMILIAR WILL sssSOON FALL!

23

WELL, NOW...

...GLAD TO SEE I HAVEN'T LOST ME TOUCH AFTER ALL THESE YEARS...

OH 'ECK, I ALMOST FORGOT — *THE YOUNG LAD!*

DON'T WORRY ABOUT ME, OLD-TIMER!

I DON'T BELIEVE IT! HOW'D YOU MANAGE TO --

NO WORRIES THERE. I JUST GOT TO THE *ROOT* OF THE PROBLEM!

GRAND TO SEE YOU, LAD! BUT WE BETTER GET A MOVE ON BEFORE THESE MONSTROSITIES RECOVER — AND NO MISTAKE!

I'M *GWELDAR THE ELDER*, BY THE WAY... AND THIS IS *GEEK*.

I'M RALF, PLEASED TO MEET YOU BOTH.

YEEP, YEEP, *YEEEP!*

WE HAVE TO GET TO THE VILLAGE AND WARN THEM!

MUM AND DAD, AND EVERYONE ELSE BACK AT THE CASTLE, I GOTTA WARN THEM TOO! MAYBE THEY CAN SEND OUT HELP!

GWELDAR, I SHOULD TELL YOU WHO I AM...

I THOUGHT YOU HAD DONE! AREN'T YOU RALF, RALF?

ANYWAY, BEST SAVE YOUR BREATH! IT'S A LONG WAY TO THE VILLAGE!

AAARRGGHH!

HELP...

HELP...

OHMYGOSH! WE'RE TOO LATE!

WHAT HAVE THEY DONE?!

YEEP...

WE CAN'T GO BACK TO THE SHACK. THAT'LL BE THE FIRST PLACE THEY'LL LOOK!

WE'LL GO TO A LITTLE PLACE I HAVE IN THE MOUNTAINS. WE'LL BE SAFE THERE...'SIDES I HAVE SOMETHING I WANT TO SHOW YOU...

NO! I HAVE TO GET BACK TO CASTLE PHEREAUX!

MY UNCLE IS RYNARDE, EARL OF PHEREAUX. HE CAN SEND OUT AN ARMY TO HELP. HE --

IT'S ALREADY TOO LATE FOR THAT, LAD! LOOK! THAT SKY BARGE IS HEADING FOR THE CASTLE! WE'LL NEVER GET THERE IN TIME TO WARN THEM!

WE'D BEST SCARPER TO THE MOUNTAINS - AND NO MISTAKE!

A **DISGRACE!** EVERY LAST ONE OF YOU!

THANK YOU, SERGEANT, BUT I WILL ADDRESS THEM NOW!

LISTEN, YOU WASTRELS, IT IS REALLY QUITE SIMPLE. IF YOU ARE NOT CAPABLE OF CAPTURING THIS OLD MAN, HIS PUP AND HIS PET, THEN THERE IS NO FUTURE IN OUR GLORIOUS ARMY FOR YOU...

...DO I MAKE MYSELF **CRYSTAL** CLEAR?

REMEMBER — IT'S YOU **SNIVELLING WRETCHES** WHO WILL BE PUNISHED IF YOU FAIL ME AGAIN.

FOR OUR PASSsT MISSsTAKESSss, WE WILL MAKE AMENDSss! WE WILL BRING THEM BACK TO YOU FOR PUNISSsHMENT, MASSsTER CHL'ATHEEIR!

...NOW GO FETCH THEM FOR ME...

The Neozord Mountain range, north of Phereaux...

HOW... MUCH... ⸘PUFF⸘ FURTHER... GWELDAR?

THE CAVE'S UP THERE ON THAT LITTLE RIDGE, SET BACK INTO THE ROCK. ANOTHER FEW MINUTES AND WE CAN REST.

YEEP...

YEP, A **CUP O' TEA** AND WE'LL ALL FEEL A LOT BETTER ABOUT THINGS...

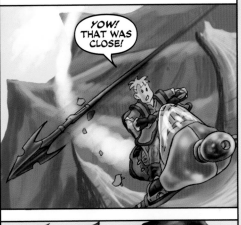

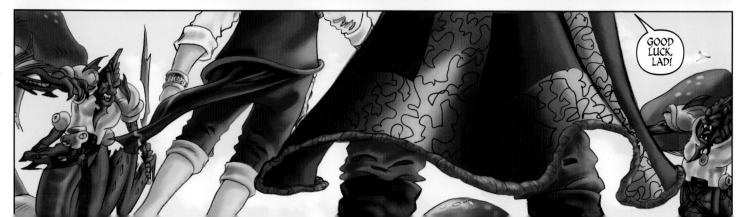

I WISH WE COULD HAVE DONE MORE TO HELP GWELDAR AND THAT GIRL BACK THERE, GEEK. BUT I GUESS THIS IS THE ONLY WAY WE'RE GONNA BEAT THOSE CREEPS!

YEEP!

WELL, ACCORDING TO THE MAP, WE'RE *HERE* - AND WE NEED TO BE OVER *THERE* AT WORLDS END! NOT SURE I LIKE THE SOUND OF THE PLACE, THOUGH, GEEK...

YEEPITY, YEEP!

I SURE HOPE GWELDAR PUT ENOUGH FUEL IN THIS THING!

MASTER CHL'ATHEEIR, I BRING WORD THAT THE LIFEBOAT HAS RETURNED. THEY DISEMBARK, EVEN AS WE SPEAK.

GOOD. TELL THEM I WISH TO SPEAK TO THE PRISONERS.

AT ONCE!

GOOD NEWS, I HOPE, CHL'ATHEEIR?

I AM SURE OF IT, LORD DHAKROSS!

...BUT THE SQUAD WILL PAY DEARLY, IF IT TURNS OUT NOT TO BE SO...

MASTER CHL'ATHEEIR REQUIRES AN AUDIENCE WITH THE PRISONERS. YOU ARE TO TAKE THEM TO HIM, FORTHWITH!

SSS! AT ONCCCE...

THIS WAY, SSSCUM - MOVE!

I'M SORRY, LASS, IN ALL THIS COMMOTION I'VE COMPLETELY FORGOTTEN MY MANNERS...

I'M GWELDAR!

AND I'M ZEPHOL! SORRY I DIDN'T GET YOU FREE IN TIME!

I'M THE ONE WHO SHOULD BE SORRY. YOU WOULDN'T BE HERE IF IT WEREN'T FOR --

OOF!

HEY, QUIT PRODDING, FANG-FEATURES...

AN AUDIENCE WITH THESSSE PRISSSONERSSS, MASSSTER CHL'ATHEEIR SSSEEKSSS!

WAIT HERE! I'LL ANNOUNCE YOUR ARRIVAL!

AH! IT'S ABOUT TIME YOU SHOWED UP! BUT WAIT - THIS IS NOT THE SAME PUP! WHERE IS...?

ELUDED USSS, HE DID.

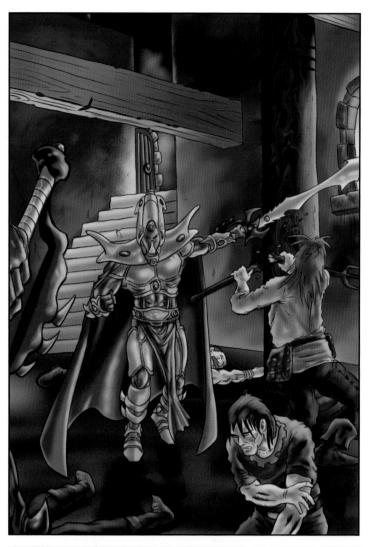

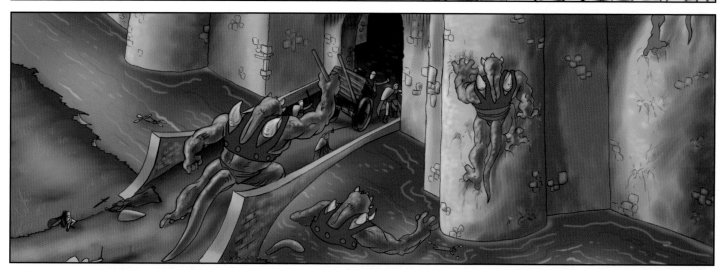

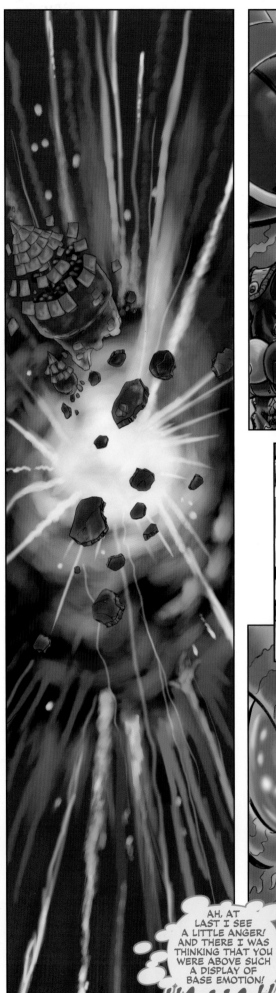

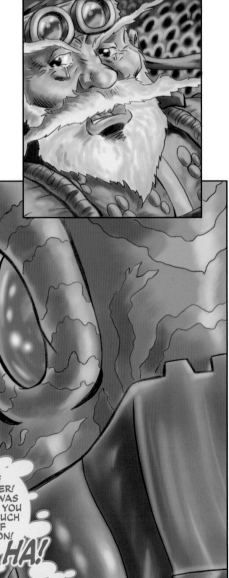

AH, AT LAST I SEE A LITTLE ANGER! AND THERE I WAS THINKING THAT YOU WERE ABOVE SUCH A DISPLAY OF BASE EMOTION!

HA HA HA!

...EVEN CASTLE PHEREAUX HAS FALLEN!

GWELDAR THE ELDER HAS SENT US ON A QUEST TO WAKE UP ALCHEMAOST THE SLEEPING CHAMPION AND WARN HIM ABOUT EVERYTHING THAT'S GOING ON!

SOUNDS LIKE SERIOUS BUSINESS. GUESS WE SHOULD SPEAK TO OLD NIALL ABOUT IT.

ERM... IF YOU SAY SO...

BUT WE HAVEN'T GOT MUCH TIME FOR A DETOUR! WE SIMPLY HAVE TO GET TO WORLDS END!

ALTHOUGH WITHOUT THE SCUD BIKE... I DON'T KNOW HOW...

TRUST ME... OLD NIALL WILL SORT THINGS OUT JUST FINE... YOU'LL SEE!

YOU TOO, LITTLE ONE! THERE'S NOTHIN' TO WORRY ABOUT!

YEEP!

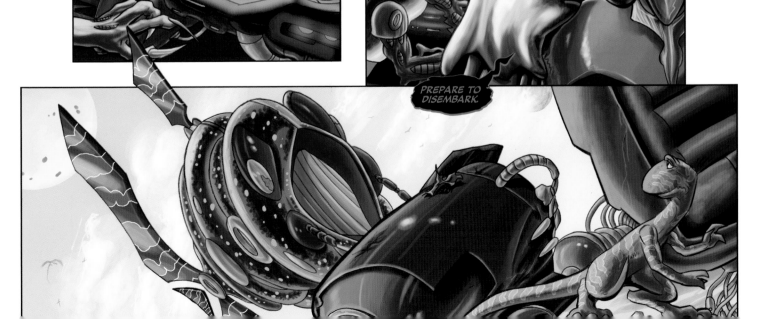

...AND WHEN THE CLOUDS PARTED, THERE IT WAS, THIS HUGE...

...AND THEN SUDDENLY GWELDAR WAVED HIS ARMS AND...

...SO AFTER WE CRASHED WE HAD TO WALK...

HERE WE ARE AT LAST!

WOW! THAT WAS QUICK! SEEMED TO TAKE HARDLY ANY TIME AT ALL!

YEEPITY, YEEP!

THAT'S BECAUSE YOU TALKED ALL THE WAY HERE!

HO THERE, NIALL! I HAVE VISITORS FOR YOU!

ELRUNN, HOW NICE TO SEE YOU AGAIN. AND I SEE YOU'VE BROUGHT SOME FRIENDS! COME IN, COME IN!

I'LL MAKE US SOMETHING TO EAT AND DRINK!

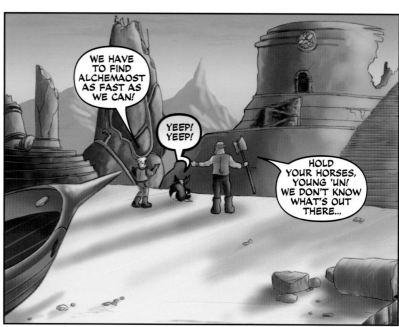

SKRUUMPETY WRUMP

Tim Perkins
Writer & Artist & Grand Wizard

Tim Perkins is an award-winning comic illustrator and writer, based in the UK, and has worked on comics as diverse as DARK DOMINION, TRANSFORMERS, THUNDERCATS, DOCTOR WHO, JUDGE DREDD, DREAMSTONE, EARTHWORM JIM, and HOT WHEELS for publishing giants such as MARVEL, DC, 2000AD, DEFIANT, and TEKNO, amongst a great many others, since 1983.

He also works as a concept artist, designer and writer in the worlds of theme park rides and animation. He lectures worldwide about comics, storytelling and creativity. He is also founder and head tutor on the Fantasy Art Unlimited art course.

He is company director of Wizards Keep Publishing, the publishing imprint of WIZARDS KEEP LIMITED.

His graphic novel WORLDS END ~ VOLUME 1 ~ THE RIDERS ON THE STORM is the first major publication from the company.

He will start work on the second volume, Worlds End ~ Volume 2 ~ A Hard Reign's Gonna Fall, in December 2011.

He currently resides in a leafy dell in the north of England with his wife, Margaret, son, Simon, his dogs Bentley and Pixie and their menagerie of other dogs, cats and fish. His daughter, Joanne has flown the Keep (pun intended) and now lives happily with her husband, Toby and their pets, but a stone's throw away.

Photo courtesy of Chris Fillingham

Yel Zamor
Colour Flats Wizard

The Russian-born Yel Zamor has had an interest in visual storytelling since childhood, but first stepped into the world of comics in 2008 after a chance encounter with Orang Utan Comics' Ian Sharman at a London-based convention. Colour work on a number of short stories appearing in OUC's FASTER THAN LIGHT anthology was to follow.

The same year, she teamed up with Tim Perkins on RELENTLESS, an atmospheric one-off book for Markosia. Yel's list of credits includes colours on HERO: 9-5, THE INTERACTIVES (2011), THE ONLY GOOD DALEK (BBC books) and a number of short stories for various publishers.

Her role on WORLDS END involved flatting, preliminary colour work.

Note from Tim:
Yel's real contribution to this book is far larger than she realises ~ without her eye for detail, speed and her ability to work as a team player, this book would not yet be complete.

Albert Deschesne
Lettering Wizard

Albert Deschesne is an artist with 18 years experience in comics. He got his start in the industry in the art department at Malibu Comics where he began colouring comics digitally by day, as part of the separation team, and colouring the old-fashioned way on the STAR TREK book DEEP SPACE NINE, as well as THE PROTECTORS and FERRET.

After leaving Malibu Comics, he went on to join Richard Starkings' Comicraft design studio and has worked on such notable books as: AVENGERS, IRON MAN, FANTASTIC FOUR and THUNDERBOLTS for Marvel Comics, as well as ACTION COMICS, SUPERMAN, SUPERGIRL and SUPERMAN/BATMAN for DC Comics and has lettered literally thousands of pages for other Marvel and DC books as well as many other publishers.

Note from Tim:
Albert's contribution to this book is to add the special Comicraft 'look' to the lettering ~ to make the words flow without standing out from the pages. The subtlety and attention to detail in his lettering makes him a great addition to the Worlds End team.

Paul Finch
Alien Motifs Wizard

Paul has always enjoyed reading comics, and his love of them enabled him to obtain a first class degree in Graphic Design.

He first met Tim at a Fantasy Art Class, Fantasy Art Unlimited, which Tim founded, that his then friend (now wife) suggested he attend. Since then, Paul has been practising his graphic design skills with his own store on Cafepress, Serendipity_UK, where his television knowledge is transformed into desirable designs.

Note from Tim:
Paul's contribution to this book is far more important than he realises. His otherworldly graphics helped me to achieve a

JAMES HILL
Editor Wizard

James Hill is a writer-editor with 25 years experience in comic and magazine creation. He has worked for many publishers, including Marvel UK, Egmont, Western Publishing and Keesing, writing stories for such internationally recognised brands as TRANSFORMERS, MASTERS OF THE UNIVERSE, MY LITTLE PONY, THE MUPPETS, THE SMURFS, DONALD DUCK, SPIDER-MAN and POWER RANGERS. For sixteen years he was Editor-in-Chief at Toontastic Publishing (formerly Just Publishing) where he supervised the development and launch of numerous monthly magazines, including CARTOON NETWORK, LOONEY TUNES, BUTT-UGLY MARTIANS, RUGRATS, THE LUCKY BAG COMIC, HOT WHEELS and BEYBLADE.

A range of bagged poster magazines based around hit movies such as PIRATES OF THE CARIBBEAN, THE DARK KNIGHT and THE INCREDIBLE HULK was a UK newstrade best seller. As Creative Officer of the Just Group, he developed new character concepts for exploitation in TV, Publishing and Consumer Products. He currently puts the years spent reading too many comics to good use, writing feature articles for the DC COMICS SUPER HERO COLLECTION and the CLASSIC MARVEL FIGURINE COLLECTION. His sole contribution to Tim Perkins' WORLDS END has been watching with awe and admiration as a talented creator with many years of experience forges his own path ~ embarking on a quest every bit as heroic as that undertaken by the characters in the book.

Note from Tim:
James' real contribution to this book has been as a supportive friend, from the very beginning of Wizards Keep, and as a talented colleague and first class editor for the final proofreading prior to printing. Oh, yes and he is the best editor that I have ever had the privilege of working with.

Rob Sharp
Design Wizard

As the senior member of Team Wizards Keep (Read: 'old venerable one') Rob has worked in UK comic publishing as a writer/illustrator/designer for almost 25 years, from the eclectic reprint of BATMAN magazine to the pink power of PRETTY PONY CLUB. He is proud to be one of those creators who is based 'Oop North' and didn't allow the bright lights of London to lure him out of the Shires.

Whilst still designing, he has turned his energies back to writing speculative fiction of all genres and is chasing that elusive first book deal. Meanwhile, he is in touch with his feminine side as a regular contributor to MY WEEKLY magazine published by D.C. Thomson and has just published five Kindle short story collections of Sci-Fi on Amazon, under the banner 'Amerikan Dreams'. (Shameless plug!)

Note from Tim:
Rob's contribution to this book is massive and much more than the title designer suggests. He enabled me to complete the book on schedule, something only someone highly experienced in publishing and book production could have done.

Bryan Talbot
Foreword

Bryan Talbot has produced underground and alternative comics, notably BRAINSTORM!, science fiction and superhero stories such as JUDGE DREDD, NEMESIS THE WARLOCK, TEKNOPHAGE, THE NAZZ and BATMAN: LEGENDS OF THE DARK KNIGHT.

He's worked on DC Vertigo titles including HELLBLAZER, SANDMAN, THE DREAMING and FABLES and has written and drawn the graphic novels for which he is best known including THE ADVENTURES OF LUTHER ARKWRIGHT, HEART OF EMPIRE, THE TALE OF ONE BAD RAT and ALICE IN SUNDERLAND.

In 2009 he was awarded an honorary Doctorate in Arts by Sunderland University. His last two books were GRANDVILLE and GRANDVILLE MON AMOUR, anthropomorphic steampunk detective thrillers. His next graphic novel is DOTTER OF HER FATHER'S EYES written by his wife Dr Mary M Talbot.

Note from Tim:
Bryan's support and kind words in his wonderful Foreword mean the world to me. I am pleased not only to have such a talented colleague, but most especially to call him my friend.

John Ridgway
Introduction

John has worked in comics since the 1960's. His work includes innumerable COMMANDO war stories for D.C. Thomson, short stories for WARRIOR magazine, ENID BLYTON'S FAMOUS FIVE for Guttenburghus, a run on DOCTOR WHO, TRANSFORMERS, ZOIDS and CYRIL THE EDITOR DROID for Marvel UK, JUDGE DREDD and LUKE KIRBY for 2000 AD, short stories for Eclipse Comics, HELLBLAZER, SPECTRE and MY NAME IS CHAOS graphic novel for DC Comics, INCREDIBLE HULK, THE AGENT graphic novel and PRINCE VALIANT limited series for Marvel. He is now colouring and completing AGE OF HEROES ~ a fantasy series that was originally published in black-and-white by Halloween and Image Comics and left incomplete ~ and is now being published in STRIP MAGAZINE by Print Media Publications, and will later be published in graphic album form.

PS, Can we please have Bentley stop following him around?

Note from Tim:
John's support throughout my career and especially during my time with Wizards Keep and working on Worlds End, along with his kind words in his Introduction mean more than mere words can say. Not only has John been mentor to me in the early days, he is also the best friend I have in comics, something I am really proud to say.

Bentley 'Bogtrotter'
Familiar & Trainee Wizard

Tim's Dog, Bentley, a little Yorkshire Terrier, arrived on the scene on July 9th 2008 and has been his best buddy since. He spends most of his days with him in the Wizards Keep studio, where one can also find his bed, toys and doggy treats. The nickname 'Bogtrotter' comes from his love of getting wet amongst the many ferns in the family gardens.

Note from Tim:
Bentley's companionship makes Wizards Keep a much more wonderful place to work.

I have loved the sequential art form of the comic book for as long as I can remember.

As a child, I consumed all manner of comics, annuals and novels, as many as my parents could give me. Around eight-years-old I was mesmerised by one comic creator in particular, although I would not realise it was the same man producing all my favourite comics until I was a little older. That guy was Jack 'King' Kirby and his art was to be an enormous influence and have a profound affect on my own work.

In the mid-eighties, I fulfilled my dream of working in comics and began freelancing for Marvel UK. Soon I began working for most of the major publishers in the field: DC, Marvel US, 2000AD, London Editions, Fleetway, Defiant, Tekno, plus a great many others... The list was endless.

I have been lucky in my career to have the opportunity to work alongside and strike up friendships with some of the most talented creative folks in the comics business, but the friendship most dear to me is the one with my mentor, John Ridgway. His invaluable advice in my early career, and his friendship throughout the years, means more than anything to me. If anyone has influenced how I approach my storytelling as much as Jack Kirby, it is John.

You know you are finally accepted as a part of the industry when someone as talented as Bryan Talbot asks his Editor-in-Chief to hire you to ink his books, and when I first heard that Bryan had done just this, upon receiving a phone call from Tekno Comics Editor, Ed Polgardy, I cannot express the immense sense of joy I felt.

I was so pleased when both John and Bryan agreed to write their Introduction and Foreword respectively. It is a great honour for me to have them included like this in my first ever Wizards Keep-published book.

I was lucky and survived the comics implosion of the mid-nineties, but as the years came and went, I realised that I would never get the chance to tell my own stories within the comics industry. I was drawn to pastures new in the field of Conceptual Art, first in the wonderful world of Theme Parks, and then later, in Animation.

I had always wanted to be able to tell the stories that resided inside my head. It became apparent to me, however, having spoken to a great many 'name' artists (and seen the wonderful work inside their portfolios that would never see print), that I would not be able to do this through one of the major comics publishers.

The lure of using my imagination ~ something that I had been called on to do less and less during my later years in comics, was too much to resist... and in 1999 I said goodbye to comics, forever... or so I thought.

I was coaxed back into producing some more comics work in the early part of the new millennium, around 2004, by my good friend, James Hill, who was then Editor-in-Chief at Toontastic Publishing ~ the very same person I chose to help proofread and edit this book.

It was around this time that I began to feel the urge to return to my true roots and I began work on a project that I had formularised some years before. That project turned into the graphic album you now hold in your hands.

Worlds End has quite a bit of history, which dates back to the early/mid seventies when everyone had long hair, wore frayed flairs and listened to Progressive Rock.

It was amongst this fused atmosphere of fantasy-rich magic and music that I first saw the phrase that would lead to this day. In the 'recommend books' listings in a novel that I was reading at school, I saw the title: 'The Well at World's End.'

There was something magical and epic about that title and it struck a chord within my artistically developing soul. I never managed to find and read the mysterious book, but the title alone sounded fascinating... and stayed with me.

It was while working as an artist for Marvel

Comics, back around 1987, that I first formulated a storyline based on the image that I had in my head of Worlds End.

The plot was joined by a dozen ~ or more ~ drawings of the characters from the story, and then Worlds End lay in limbo, like so many other ideas, as I forged ahead with my career as a professional comic book and conceptual artist.

Eventually, as I hung about the studio between jobs in the animation field, I decided that I would like to work (at long last) on a book of my own. When I thought again about Worlds End, it just felt right... and so I set to work fleshing out the plot and redesigning, if only slightly, the characters.

I set up my company, Wizards Keep, in March 2005, as a vehicle to publish the stories and to produce the related merchandise based on my new world.

Now, I am a firm believer in serendipity, and only a year (or so) back I once again came across the title that I had first seen in the seventies: 'The Well at World's End.' I had been running a search of keywords to see how the company and products were ranking on the Internet search engines, when low and behold, it came up as part of the search, several pages in.

The website contained some extracts from the book, and so I read a little... and you can imagine my surprise to discover that the lead character was called Ralf, just like mine here in Worlds End. Now, bearing in mind that I had only seen the book's title before this, you can appreciate my amazement. The hairs on the back of my neck stood on end, and I experienced a great example of serendipity.

I hoped then, as now, that it was a good omen.

My wife, Margaret, daughter, Joanne, son, Simon, my parents, Harry and Grace and close family and friends have all shared my journey with the characters from Worlds End. They have had to share my time, as well, as I worked on the saga, for which I am eternally grateful. Without their support, I would not have been able to get to this point. It has been a long journey for everyone, but now the first volume is complete and I hope the time will seem well spent.

In addition to the contributions made by John, Bryan and James, the creative individuals backing me on this project are a dream team, many of whom I have worked with in the past...

The lettering is by Comicraft's supremely talented Albert Deschesne, ably supported by lettering maestro and Comicraft's President and First Tiger, Richard Starkings. Book design and page layouts have been provided by Rob Sharp, an artist in his own right, who has worked with my comic strips for at least two decades. Paul Finch, an ex~student of mine designed the wonderful alien motifs on the Title Verso and Contents pages. And last, but certainly not least, my wonderful colour assistant is Yel Zamor, whose flat colouring gave me a great foundation to work on ~ her attention to detail is amazing.

Worlds End was not the idea I would have used originally, when I first envisioned creating a company like Wizards Keep back in the seventies, but it seemed an appropriate idea for the new millennium. The story came from the heart, like all the best stories. It wrote itself, almost as if I was linked to the folk of Gaeyrth, psychically, and was only re~telling their amazing saga.

The characters from Worlds End have grown to be a virtual extension of my family, nowadays. Their trials and tribulations affect me like those of my real family. A long journey stretches out before young Ralf ~ as he slowly comes of age throughout the series.

Worlds End is an epic saga, which will take time to tell, and I hope you will enjoy reading the tale as much as I enjoy telling it. I also hope you will think enough of the characters to return here, when Volume 2 is finished, to see their fate, now left hanging in the balance...

Tim Perkins
England
August 2011

Welcome to Gaeyrth

Welcome to the weird and wonderful world of Gaeyrth, the planet that is home to the mysterious place known as Worlds End.

It is here that young Ralf and his allies, Gweldar the Elder, his familiar, Geek, and a girl they meet early in their adventures called Zephol, fight to keep their world safe from the invading hordes of alien interlopers known as the Aoevill.

This is a world 'untainted by evil.' A world whose peoples have not known war for two centuries, and where the art of battle has been long~since forgotten.

When Last War ended, a provision was put in place to stop another conflict from erupting again. The wizards of old placed the greatest warrior of the time into a magikal sleep, to be awoken, if and when the need arose. Worlds End is the resting~place of Alchemaost, that sleeping champion.

Here then, nestled amidst the many hamlets, villages, towns and shires of Gaeyrth, new battles are to be fought and friendships forged as the saga of Worlds End unfolds.

The Aoevill hordes believe they have an easy task of aqua~forming the tranquil planet. They have not reckoned with our heroes, however, who are determined to outwit the high~tech machinations of the invading aliens, armed with just their courage, and a little help from magikal means.

The guards of Gaeyrth are a token force, at best, and are more of a police constabulary than an army strong enough to repel alien invaders, especially those with such amazing capabilities.

Try to imagine soldiers from a bygone medieval era, here on our own world, having to face such scientifically advanced forces. Only then will you understand the depths of terror felt by the people of Gaeyrth.

The saga of Worlds End will be a long and eventful ~ filled with trials and tribulations that even our four heroic friends may find insurmountable

Artwork Outtakes

Finding the right style for a new comic book or graphic novel can be a tricky process for an artist. From the very beginning, the right atmosphere has to be created ~ layouts decided upon and the characters clearly established within an often unique environment.

While working on Worlds End, I had a false start with the layout for the very first page of the story. Below is my early attempt at drawing the page. It is clearly very different from what appears on page two of the tale you have just read.

There's nothing wrong with the artwork, as such, but the page doesn't give the reader a true sense of the scale and appearance of Gweldar's shack. It contains some of the elements I wanted to show ~ but not enough and without the necessary 'wow' factor.

Panel Three is almost the same as in the printed version... but pulling back the camera from this close~up version allowed me to establish even more of the setting. Panel One on the 'outtake' became Panel Two in the finished version, albeit a few seconds further on in time, as Geek knocks over the bowl of porridge.

Not much of a difference, but I was able to add a 'new' first panel ~ firmly establishing the location in the mind of the readers, and setting the character of Gweldar clearly within it. There was

now no mistaking that we were looking at the inside of a very unique cottage. Along with the later shot of the two characters 'cleaning the drive,' this established Gweldar's shack as a 'real' location ~ a clearly defined building in a clearly illustrated locale. This gave the whole page greater realism ~ and provided a suitably authentic 'stage' upon which the characters could 'act.'

That I only ever drew two panels of this version of the page, suggests that I was not happy with the layout from the very beginning.

The difference with the way I have been able to work on the graphic novel, as opposed to a regular comic, is that I have been able to sit back and take stock. At each stage, I've been able to tweak the pages to make them work better. There would never be time to do this on a weekly or monthly comic book.

This very simple, yet necessary, layout change set a precedent for the rest of the book. Funnily enough, it made the creation of the remainder of the story very easy for me, at least as far as the layouts were concerned.

Hopefully, this 'outtake' shows that when it just doesn't feel right... then it is probably wiser to start all over again... until it does.

The Good Guys

GWELDAR THE ELDER:
Gweldar is a kind and bumbling mage. He is a Mathemagician who uses limited magic. He has the ability to use more powerful incantations, but his memory for spells is not what it was. He quite often ends a sentence with the phrase "...and no mistake!"

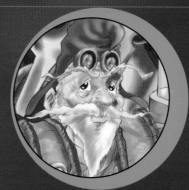

GEEK:
Geek is Gweldar's mischievous familiar and best friend. He is a most loyal creature that has been with Gweldar since the mage became a fully fledged Mathemagician.

RALF:
Ralf is the nephew of Rynarde Earl of Phereaux, the shire in which we start the story. His uncle's castle overlooks the nearby village of Ruune, where Gweldar lives. Along with his parents and an entourage, Ralf is visiting from a neighbouring shire to the west; a place called Xellos.

ZEPHOL:
Zephol is a young girl that Gweldar, Geek and Ralf meet early on their quest. She is the more street-wise of the two children, and quite capable of looking after herself. She is the mysterious one of our group of heroes.

ELRUNN:
This middle-aged woodcutter kindly takes Ralf and Geek to meet a friend of his when trouble strikes the Scud-Bike they are travelling on.

NIALL:
Niall is an old inventor and enthusiast of all things archaic.

The Bad Guys

THE AOEVILL:

The Aoevill are an aquatic, war~like race from a far away galaxy. They have outgrown their own watery realms and seek to conquer and aqua~form other planets to fulfil their needs, hence their arrival on Gaeyrth. The High Host is the main fleet of the Aoevill race, commanded by Lord Gralltharr.

LORD DHAKROSS:

Lord Dhakross is second~in~command of the Aoevill race. He is the son of Lord Gralltharr and as such, is Prince Regent.

MASTER CHL'ATHEEIR:

Master Chl'atheeir is the leader of the elite~fighting force known as Val'quath, which means The Shadow Warriors in their native tongue.

SERGEANT QU'AELTOS:

Sergeant Qu'aeltos is Master Chl'atheeir's second~in~command and is the sole survivor of a world from a previous invasion.

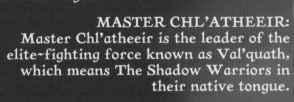

ADJUTANT R'CHLANNE:

Adjutant R'chlanne is one of the formidable Shadow Warriors. Well versed in the dark arts and combat, he makes for a very formidable opponent.

STORM SERPENTS:

The Storm Serpents are a race of deadly serpents, allied to the Aoevill. They are a skilled fighting force and form the front line of the Aoevill army.

SKELOR:

The Skelor are a race of incredibly deadly warriors. They are sent in to subjugate unwilling worlds such as Gaeyrth, as an advanced warrior force.

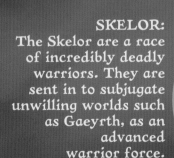

HARVESTERS:

The Harvesters are a race of carnivorous warriors. They are used to eradicate enemy forces when it would be too costly to use normal squads of Shadow Warriors or Storm Serpents.

LORD GRALLTHARR:

Lord Gralltharr is the ruler of the Aoevill. He is similar in appearance to Lord Dhakross. His fleet form the High Host.

All that remained for Gweldar to do, having successfully completed and passed all the trials and tests of his knowledge and skills, was to pick his familiar ~ just as the ancient Wizard~Kings had done centuries ago. Most of his contemporaries had already picked their companions, nearly all choosing the larger, potentially more aggressive familiars, or those creatures knowledgeable in the dark arts.

Rising from his chair, he strode towards the room that housed the hatchlings. He wondered just how many of his kind had walked this very path over the centuries. He was so lost in thought that before he knew it, he was standing outside the heavy oak door, behind which lay his future partner in the art of Mathemagiks.

The tradition of the Rite of Choosing the Familiar had been handed down through countless millennia, and hardly a word, or action had been changed during all that time. Gweldar eyed the wooden door and spoke a magikal spell in a tongue long since forgotten by mortal men ~ but then, Gweldar was no longer a mortal man. He was, after all, a budding Mathemagician, newly graduated from the high ranks of the Wizardry Academy.

The words flowed from his mouth like music, piercing, yet soothing at the same time. The glow from the flames of a wall~mounted torch, to his left and slightly above his head, accentuated his hawkish features. At length, as his words evaporated into the aether, the door opened before him with a creak and a hiss, as though all the air within had escaped.

The room beyond, which housed the hatchlings, was dark ~ lit only by the dim light of a few candles. There was a sweetness and a stillness in the air… and an ambience to the environment within. The Mathemagician strode inside to make his choice.

Gweldar walked around the room, taking time to stop and observe each of the hatchlings in turn. There were all manner of creatures present, from frogs and toads, to snails with three heads and worms with two legs. There were plenty of larger beasts, too, like winged Griffins, Manticores, and even Dragons; young of course, as they were all fresh hatchlings.

The novice Mathemagician stroked his bearded chin, all the while pondering his choice. Should it be a small fellow, or a larger one, he mused to himself. Gweldar went around again, stopping at an owl. He quite like birds, but as the owl rolled its eyes and opened its beak ready to bite him, he realised that birds didn't like him! And no mistake!

Deciding not to make this be~feathered creature his choice he continued around the room, stopping at a small dragon. He liked dragons, too. The dragon eyed him, a small plume of smoke coming from each of its two nostrils. Gweldar went to pat the creature on the head ~ and shot backwards as a blistering plume of flame erupted from the dragon's mouth. Perhaps not, thought Gweldar. After all, he could hardly be seen repairing fire~damage caused by his familiar. That would be unseemly and certainly not befitting a newly~ appointed Mathemagician. Dragons were obviously too hot to handle.

At length he stopped again, as he came upon a magnificent specimen of a Chimera. It's long green main glistened in the pale glare of the candlelight. It purred as Gweldar went to stroke its head. Ah, at last, this one seemed to like him. He went to unclip the leather leash, which tethered the Chimera to an iron post inside the small arena in which it sat. The Chimera wrapped its serpentine tail around Gweldar's arm, as he slowly removed the leash from the post.

Gweldar picked up the Chimera's small goat~like body, and placed it at his feet. Then, with the leash in hand, he began to lead the creature from the room. They had barely crossed half the distance to the doorway, when a large Basilisk suddenly broke free from its chains. The savage creature leapt from its resting~place ~ and landed in front of Gweldar and the Chimera, blocking their exit.

Both creatures reared and hissed and spat their venom at each other. The Basilisk tried to make eye contact with the Chimera, hoping to kill the smaller creature instantly with its deadly vision. At the same time, the large serpentine creature let loose a spray of poisonous breath. Gweldar dropped the leash and covered his mouth as the green vapour swirled madly about him.

Suddenly, both creatures turned on the Mathemagician, who staggered back, in shock at such a ferocious attack. The vapour was having an affect on his ability to think. He blinked and shook his head in a desperate attempt to clear his thoughts. He found himself having to dodge not only the noxious green breath and whipping tail of the Basilisk, but also the intense flame of the Chimera.

Gweldar was trying to put together a spell to rid himself of the bothersome monsters, when a furry creature with a bushy tail jumped up from one of the hatchling seating areas. Despite its lack of stature, the little fellow valiantly came to the defence of the Mathemagician.

The creature wrapped its little arms and legs around the roaring Basilisk's neck, and used its bushy tail to fend off the confused Chimera. Thanks to the hatchlings timely intervention, Gweldar was finally able to concentrate. He remembered, at last, an incantation that he had learned many years ago, in his second week at the Wizardry Academy. Gweldar recited the spell ~ and as his words slowly faded away, so too did the fighting before him. Both the Basilisk and the Chimera fell asleep at his feet.

The little creature was unaffected by Gweldar's incantation ~ and thankfully its fur had only been lightly singed by the Chimera's fiery breath. It sighed a deep sigh, and looked up at Gweldar. It seemed to smile happily, as it curled its tail around the Mathemagician's leg.

Gweldar returned the smile, kneeling so that he was at eye level with his rescuer. The creature squeaked a low "Yeep," as Gweldar placed his arms about it in thanks and recognition of its bravery.

"Well, little fellow," said Gweldar, "I think I should put these two back where I found them. An' then I guess I should get on with choosing a proper familiar ~ and no mistake!" But as his eyes met those of the small creature, Gweldar knew that the choice had already been made...

"You picked me, didn't you, fella?" he said. "And you know what? I agree! I think we'll make a great team, you and me. You're now a Mathemagician's Familiar! How would you like to be called Geek?"

Leaping into Gweldar's arms, Geek gave the wizard a big hug

~ at least as big as his small size would allow!

And with that, Gweldar and Geek marched out of the dimly~lit room. They left the darkness behind them, heading towards a bright, new tomorrow. It was just the start of a long and unique friendship, filled with excitement and adventure...

...And no mistake!

The Beginning...

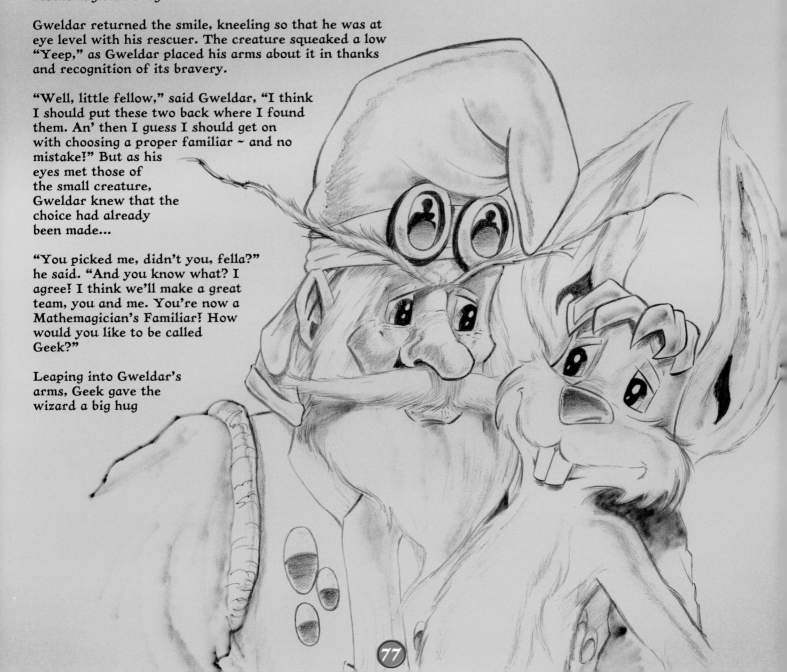

Que'lldro'ss is the name of a giant spiral galaxy. On the outer limbs of one of its great arms lies the Squatsretch star system.

The planets' orbits are all affected by the eccentric, sometimes elliptical orbits of the three stars, and also their planetary neighbours.

The triple star Squatsretch system consists of the following three suns and their accompanying planets...

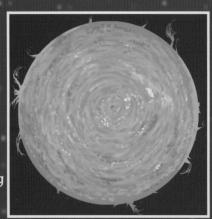

Squatsretch is the largest of the three suns and it is a red hyper~giant around which the other two suns and accompanying planets revolve.

It also has its own three large gas giants and seven smaller planets revolving around it.

The rest of the planetary system consists of rock~based worlds...

Y'Cthinia is a blue~hued planet

Xo'Tolos is a pale~blue planet

Jac'Obirol is a green~and~blue world almost as large as Cydnamoria

W'wrell is a small grey planet

O'ryioth is a huge orange hyper~giant, and the largest and most violently storm~active of Squatsretch's gaseous planets

Cydnamoria is the largest of the rocky planets and has a warm orange hue

Ruulle is a yellow gas giant with green and white storm clouds

Vithanius is a green~hued planet

Myr'nriol is a blue gas giant and the smallest of the three

G'Anyreanos is a violent black and red planet full of volcanic activity

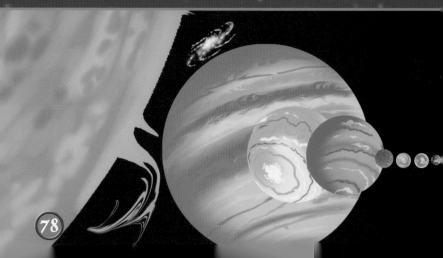

Squatsretch System

Exxotryll is the middle~sized of the three suns and it is a yellow sun that is slightly larger than our own Sol. Its ten planets mainly rotate around it in a counter~clockwise retrograde orientation.

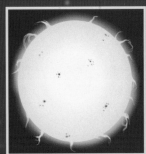

Ylliaad is a giant green gas giant

Aeynied is a purple gas giant

Aeryiell is the smallest of the inner~most plants. Uninhabited due to its close proximity to the largest of the three suns, this little pink~hued planet is practically hidden by its huge parent star

Prot'orius is a star~like pseudo~planet, whose yellow hue and back spots are caused by atmospheric disturbances

Uranddor is a larger planet than Aeryiell, and is only slightly smaller than Gaeyrth. Its blue hue sets it apart from its sister planets

Randyll is another habitable planet like Gaeyrth

Gaeyrth is the third inner~most planet within the Squatsretch system. It is a small unassuming world, innocuous but for one wonderful fact ~ that it harbours life. It is home to a myriad of different races and creatures. The adventures we follow take place, for the most part, on this world

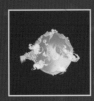

Bry'llonn is a red~hued rock~based barren planet

Kryxx'll is a blue~green planet ~ pretty inhospitable with a methane rich atmosphere.

N'roll is a small, moon~like rocky planet

Que'll is the smallest of the three suns and is a white dwarf. It has three planets that orbit around it ~ two in a clockwise rotation with the third in a tight elliptical orbit from right to left and at a 35° angle to the star's north facing pole.

C'hlorinth is a small, grey pseudo~planet

F'ornithyll is yellow~and~red Gaeyrth~sized planet

Th'Ornitnoww is the largest of this star's rock~based planets

LIFEBOAT:
Lifeboats are the small craft used by the Aoevill race to send elite squads of fighting units down to a planet's surface.
Basilisk class.

BATTLE BARGE:
Battle Barges are huge crafts, housing the armies and arsenals of the Aoevill race. They are capable of space travel and carry an incredible array of external weaponry.
Leviathan class.

THRESHER:
Threshers are mid-sized ships, each capable of transporting legions of warriors for the Aoevill race. They are capable of space travel and are equipped with highly-destructive weaponry. They come in a variety of shapes and sizes.
Chimaera class.

WORLD SHAKER:
World Shakers are the Aoevill's aqua-forming doomsday machines. They are as large as some small planetoids.
Destroyer class.

DROP-SHIPS:
Drop-ships are mid-sized ships that are used to transport the hordes of Skelor and Harvesters onto the surface of unsuspecting worlds in readiness for aqua-forming.
Cetacean class.

ARK:
The Ark is a huge craft that can house the entire invasion fleet of the Aoevill race. It is capable of space travel, and has enough fire power to lay waste to entire worlds. It is also capable of linking with ~ and towing ~ World Shaker machines.
Behemoth class.

BIOMINES:
Biomines are floating, highly volatile creatures. They are used by the Aoevill to ward off unwanted approaches. If touched, these creatures may explode, fire lethal projectiles (which can, in turn, be explosive or filled with acid) or secrete acidic venom.

THE MIND MASSAGER:
The Mind Massager is the pseudo-eldritch machine used by the Shadow Warriors to extract information from the minds of an enemy.

ION-SPLICERS:
Weapons of mass destruction used by the Aeovill.

MATHEMAGIKS:
The science of numeracy and its magikal connotations.

HAERAH-KEY:
A magikal key, that only Grand Mages can invoke the power of, in order to open portals.

A GATHER-RING:
A Ring of magik that draws things together... like an eldritch Black Hole.

SCUD-BIKES:
Low flying vehicles that Gweldar, Ralf and others are able to ride upon.

TELL-ME-VISION:
A magikal box for viewing events from a distance.

Inside the Keep

People are always asking what it is like working inside Wizards Keep. And my answer? It's magikal!

And so, because a picture paints a thousand words...

...and my keyboard needs a rest, here are a few shots of the studio set-up and some of the other rooms inside the Keep.

A step-by-step guide to how Worlds End came to life ~ from basic concept to the finished book you now hold in your hands.

I am forever being asked what the process is for me nowadays, when I am producing comic book art. Well, although the process differs slightly when I am working for another company ~ this is how I have produced Worlds End...

The concept was conceived way back in the eighties, when I had just begun working for Marvel Comics. At that time, I drew some rough sketches, and made extensive notes on the possible characters and story elements.

In 2003, when I was thinking about publishing my first graphic novel, I decided on the Worlds End concept. I needed a vehicle to launch the project and therefore created my own company, Wizards Keep.

The way I work is quite simple and goes something like this...

Page 37

187. Ralf, Geek and their newfound friend, Elrunn are on their way to a man called Niall. They are walking through the forest.

RALF: ...and when the clouds parted, there it was, this huge...

188. They walk past a waterfall, still inside the forest.

RALF: ...and then suddenly Gweldar waved his arms and...

189. They climb up some rocks, still inside the forest.

RALF: ...so after we crashed we had to walk...

190. Until at length they reach the edge of the forest and a small clearing. Inside the clearing is a stone built cottage with a wood slat and shingle roof. By this time it is late afternoon.

ELRUNN: Here we are at last!

RALF: Wow! That was quick! Seemed to take hardly any time at all!

GEEK: Yeepity, yeep!

191.Elrunn calls out to Niall as they approach the cottage.

ELRUNN: That's because you talked all the way here!

JOINED: Ho there, Niall! I have visitors for you!

192. C/U of an old man with a big beaming smile on his face welcoming them.

NIALL: Elrunn, how nice to see you again. And I see you've brought some friends! Come in, come in!

JOINED: I'll make us something to eat and drink

Once I have my plot thought out (I usually write notes over a long period of time), I write the script; not in too much detail, but enough so that I can remember everything ~ this includes all the dialogue. On Worlds End, the emphasis was on having each character speaking in a unique way... and communicating these distinct voices to the reader.

The script is then read many times, by the editor and me, to proofread it and to iron out any mistakes with spelling, grammar and characterisation.

Next, I produce a blueline pencil drawing. I prefer

blue, as it is always cleaner. I work very light at first and then tighten things up.

I then scan the blue pencils into the computer and convert them into greyscale using Photoshop. I adjust the brightness and contrast levels, until I am happy with the finished appearance.

I next set about laying in all the flat colours as a base, although early on with this first volume, I decided upon a new route ~ I hired a colour flats assistant in the form of Yel Zamor to enable me to make up time.

Once this stage is done, I then add one or two shadows to give me a feel for the mood.

Then I really start to add the form by adding shadow and light to create a reality, even though my style here is very cartoony.

I keep adding the light and dark to the page until I am happy with the overall balance. As I go along, I add things like the Jacob's ladder lighting effect, seen as the sunlight shines through the blinds to Gweldar the Mathemagician's cottage as seen on page 1 of the strip.

I then continue to apply the colours until I am totally happy with the finished artwork, (although a few weeks later I may look at it and think, oh why did I do that?).

I don't think you ever truly finish a piece of artwork; you simply leave it to pursue another.

Once all the pages are finished, including the cover and other none comic strip features, I create special computer folders for each one. These folders contain the illustrations, plus all the necessary graphics, text pieces and fonts.

This enables me to import the pages into InDesign.

Once all the pages are in that Adobe program, they go through a process called 'Pre~Flight' ~ which uses software to check for any discrepancies or computer errors, such as incorrectly~sized pictures or words that have suddenly disappeared!

Then, all that remains is for me to e~mail the completed computer files to the printers ~ this volume was printed in Bosnia.

Finally, comes the checking of the printer's proofs by the editor and myself... and then it's a case of sitting back and waiting for the finished books to be shipped back here to Wizards Keep in the UK.

I hope you enjoyed this little trip around my current working practises, and that it answers some of the questions about the digital paintwork techniques used to create Worlds End.

Once the actual illustration is completed to my satisfaction, I usually go in and add the word balloons and captions ~ although with Worlds End, I decided to employ the best guys in the business, those wonderful wizards of the fonts, Comicraft, to produce the lettering and sound effects.

The characters for Worlds End were created back in the mid to late eighties, along with a whole slew of concepts for other kinds of books.

The characters all languished, as is the way of these things, until I was looking at which of my ideas I wanted to turn into the first graphic novel published under the Wizards Keep imprint.

There have ben very few changes made to the characters since I first drew them all those years ago. The most significant alteration has probably been made to Ralf ~ who now sports a completely different haircut.

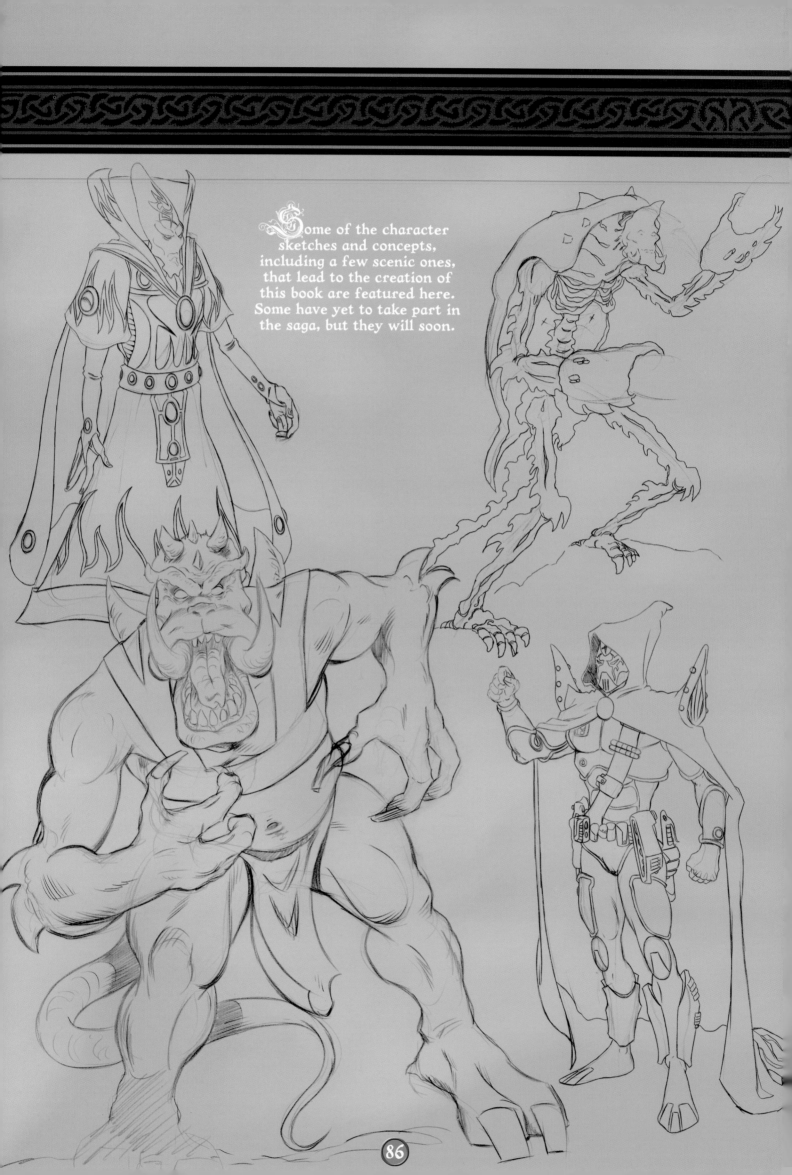

Some of the character
sketches and concepts,
including a few scenic ones,
that lead to the creation of
this book are featured here.
Some have yet to take part in
the saga, but they will soon.

I hope you enjoy this little foray into the behind~the~ scenes development of Worlds End.